THE COMPLETE

JOSEPH AND THE AMAZING TECHNICOLOR® DREAMCOAT

MUSIC BY ANDREW LLOYD WEBBER • LYRICS BY TIM RICE

CHRIS TOLLEY FOR THE REALLY USEFUL GROUP LTD.
PRODUCTION PHOTOGRAPHS BY TRISTRAM KENTON

THE COMPLETE

JOSEPH AND THE AMAZING TECHNICOLOR® DREAMCOAT
MUSIC BY ANDREW LLOYD WEBBER • LYRICS BY TIM RICE

ACT ONE

ACT TWO

ANDREW
LLOYD
WEBBER

Andrew Lloyd Webber is the composer of *The Likes of Us*, *Joseph and the Amazing Technicolor® Dreamcoat*, *Jesus Christ Superstar*, *By Jeeves*, *Evita*, *Variations* and *Tell Me On A Sunday* (later combined as *Song & Dance*), *Cats*, *Starlight Express*, *The Phantom of the Opera*, *Aspects of Love*, *Sunset Boulevard*, *Whistle Down the Wind*, *The Beautiful Game* and *The Woman in White*. He composed the film scores of *Gumshoe* and *The Odessa File*, and a setting of the Latin Requiem Mass, *Requiem*.

In 2004 he produced a film version of *The Phantom of the Opera* directed by Joel Schumacher and in 2009 he will premiere his sequel to *The Phantom of the Opera* which will be directed by the award-winning director Jack O'Brien.

In 2006 he oversaw a new production of *Evita* in London, a unique version of *The Phantom of the Opera* in Las Vegas and pioneered television casting for musical theatre with the hit BBC series *How Do You Solve A Problem Like Maria?*, which searched for a Maria in *The Sound of Music*. The series won an International Emmy. He repeated his success with *Any Dream Will Do* which cast the title role of *Joseph and the Amazing Technicolor® Dreamcoat* and he will cast the musical *Oliver!* for the BBC later this year.

He currently owns seven London theatres including the Theatre Royal Drury Lane and the London Palladium.

His awards include seven Tonys, three Grammys including Best Contemporary Classical Composition for *Requiem*, seven Oliviers, a Golden Globe, an Oscar, two International Emmys, the Praemium Imperiale, the Richard Rodgers Award for Excellence in Musical Theatre and the Kennedy Center Honor.

He was knighted in 1992 and created an honorary life peer in 1997.

TIM RICE

Tim Rice (Lyrics) was born in 1944. He began songwriting in 1965 in which year his first song *That's My Story* (tune as well as words) was recorded by a rock group called the Nightshift whose career never recovered. That same year he met fellow budding songwriter Andrew Lloyd Webber whose musical ambitions were in theatre rather than rock or pop. They teamed up and wrote four musicals together from 1965–1978. The first, *The Likes of Us* (1965–6) was performed for the first time in 2005 and became available on CD, a mere 40 years after its creation. The other three, *Joseph and the Amazing Technicolor® Dreamcoat* (1968), *Jesus Christ Superstar* (1969–71) and *Evita* (1976–78) were more immediate successes.

Feeling certain that they could never top this lot, the pair went their separate ways in the early eighties, whereupon ALW immediately topped that lot with *Cats*. Tim Rice then wrote *Blondel* (1983), a mediaeval romp, with Stephen Oliver, which ran for a year in London but not for long elsewhere. This was followed in 1986 by *Chess*, in collaboration with ABBA's Björn Ulvaeus and Benny Andersson. *Chess* had a healthy run in the West End but flopped on Broadway, the New York Times bloke being particularly forceful in his disapproval. In 1989 Tim translated the famous French musical *Starmania* (by Michel Berger and Luc Plamondon) into English, which resulted in a number one album – in France. In the nineties he worked primarily and happily with the Disney empire, contributing lyrics to the movies *Aladdin* (music by Alan Menken) and *The Lion King*, (music by Elton John and Hans Zimmer) and to the stage shows *Beauty and the Beast* (Alan Menken), *The Lion King* and *Aida* (both Sir Elton). Between Disney commitments he wrote the words for Cliff Richard's theatrical blockbuster *Heathcliff* (music by John Farrar), which toured the UK in 1995–96.

He is currently reworking an operatic musical he has written with Alan Menken (*King David*), and on new treatments of *Chess*, the New York Times bloke having been replaced. In 2007 he wrote the lyrics for eight songs for the film *Nutcracker – The Untold Story* (with music by Tchaikovsky) to be released towards the end of 2008. He has just completed a new stage work about the life of Machiavelli.

Since 1991 he has been Chairman of the Foundation for Sport and the Arts which has distributed over £100 million to sporting and artistic causes. He has won a variety of awards, mainly for the wrong things, or for simply turning up. He lives in London, Cornwall and on the motorway between the two, has three children, his own cricket team and a knighthood.

JOSEPH AND THE AMAZING TECHNICOLOR DREAMCOAT®

Lyrics by Tim Rice   *Music by Andrew Lloyd Webber*

1967 Andrew Lloyd Webber and Tim Rice commissioned by Alan Doggett, head of music at Colet Court (St Paul's junior school, Hammersmith), to provide a choral work for performance as part of an end of term Easter concert.

1968 MARCH 1 • Original 15-minute version pop cantata performed at Colet Court. Novello & Co Ltd offered to publish the score.

MAY 12 • Performance at Central Hall, Westminster, now 20 minutes long. Tim Rice played Pharaoh and the pop group The Mixed Bag joined the school orchestra. *Sunday Times* Critic Derek Jewell was in the audience and wrote a review describing the show as 'a considerable piece of barrier breaking by its creators'.

NOVEMBER 9 • Now expanded to 35 minutes, the show was performed at St Paul's Cathedral.

1969 JANUARY • The first recording was released on Decca Records, conducted by Alan Doggett from Colet Court, featuring the school choir, David Daltrey and The Mixed Bag.

JANUARY 28 • Further performance at Central Hall, Westminster.

1970 MAY • The American debut performance was given at the College of the Immaculate Conception, Douglastown, Long Island.

1972 First performance as a real stage show at the Edinburgh Festival, directed by Frank Dunlop for the Young Vic Theatre Company. This production subsequently played at the Young Vic and the Round House. It was now 40 minutes long.

1973 FEBRUARY 17 • A further expanded version of Frank Dunlop's production moved into the West End's Albery Theatre (now Noël Coward Theatre) produced by Robert Stigwood. A cast recording with Gary Bond and Paul Reeves was released on the RSO label. A further expanded version was produced at the Haymarket Theatre, Leicester.

1974 MCA Records released the first recording of the 'complete work' again with Gary Bond, Peter Reeves and Gordon Waller and featuring Maynard Williams, recorded at Olympic Studios and conducted by Chris Hamel-Cooke and Andrew Lloyd Webber.

NOVEMBER 19 • PACT produced the show in South Africa, opening at the Alexander Theatre, Johannesburg, and then playing Pretoria, Natal, the Cape and Rhodesia. A recording of the show was released by EMI with Bruce Millar, Richard Loring and Alvon Collison.

1978 & 1979 Paul Jones played Joseph in Christmas seasons at the Westminster Theatre.

1979 A studio recording was made and released on EMI Records with Paul Jones as Joseph and Tim Rice as The Narrator. Bill Kenwright produced his first touring production. Subsequent casts included Jess Conrad, Mike Holoway and David Ian. The production was described as a 'Juggernaut of Joy' and toured continuously for the next 12 years.

1980 APRIL 13 • Ford's Theatre Washington, DC, opened a US production which ran for seven months.
Jess Conrad led the cast and played the Christmas season at the Vaudeville Theatre.

1981 NOVEMBER 18 • The Washington production transferred Off-Broadway to the Entermedia Theatre.
Jess Conrad returned to London for a Christmas season at Sadler's Wells.

1982 JANUARY 27 • The Washington production transferred to Broadway, opening at the Royale Theatre. Bill Hutton and Laurie Beecham headed the cast. A cast recording was released by Chrysalis on LP and CD.

1983 • The 1973 London cast recording was re-released by Polydor.

1991 JUNE 12 • The London Palladium production opened, produced by the Really Useful Theatre Company Ltd and starring Jason Donovan, directed by Steven Pimlott. The role of Joseph was subsequently played by Darren Day and Phillip Schofield. This was the first professional production to incorporate the children's choir as an integral part of the action. A recording was released on Polydor Records and Jason Donovan had a No 1 single with 'Any Dream Will Do'. In December, the 'Joseph Mega Re-Mix' reached No 13 in the charts. Phillip Schofield subsequently led the casts on an enormously successful UK tour. Aled Jones also played Joseph later in the tour. *Jozsef és a színes, szélesvásznú álomkabát* was performed and recorded for an LP in Hungary.

1992 JUNE 18 • First performance at the Elgin Theatre, Toronto, Canada, starring Donny Osmond.

1993 FEBRUARY 25 • The show opened at the Pantages Theatre, Los Angeles, starring Michael Damian.

NOVEMBER 10 • Opening night for Michael Damian and company at Broadway's Minskoff Theatre.

1994 PACT toured a new production in South Africa and *Jozef a Jeho Za'Zračný Farebný Plašť* opened in Bratislava.

1997 A brand new Bill Kenwright production began touring. In the USA, Troika Productions also mounted a spectacular new tour. *Józef I Cudowny Plazcs Snów w Technikolorze* opened in Poland.

1999 Video released by the Really Useful Group based on the London Palladium production and starring Donny Osmond, Maria Friedman, Richard Attenborough and Joan Collins. A soundtrack album was also released.

2001 The singalong version of the show was launched in the UK.

2003 FEBRUARY 13 • Bill Kenwright staged a new West End production at the New London Theatre starring Stephen Gately and later Ian 'H' Watkins. His touring production continued playing up and down the country.

2005 A cast recording was made of the Italian production, *Joseph e la Strabiliante Tunica dei Sogni Technicolor.*

2007 MARCH 31 • *Any Dream Will Do* on BBC TV launched a search for a new talent to lead the cast in a new West End production.

JUNE 9 • Lee Mead was voted as the people's choice to play Joseph. He immediately recorded 'Any Dream Will Do' which was released as a single in aid of BBC Children in Need and went to No. 2 in the charts.

JULY 17 • *Joseph and the Amazing Technicolor Dreamcoat®* opened at the Adelphi Theatre, London, in a re-worked version of the 1991 London Palladium production.

Countless other professional and amateur productions have played throughout the world since the original version was first heard in 1968.

Bill Kenwright's production has entered the *Guinness Book of Records* as the longest-running touring stage musical.

- Chronology by Mark Fox

ACT ONE

PROLOGUE

Music by ANDREW LLOYD WEBBER

Lyrics by TIM RICE

JACOB AND SONS / JOSEPH'S COAT

Music by ANDREW LLOYD WEBBER

Lyrics by TIM RICE

1. Way, way back many centuries ago, not long after the Bible began,
2. Jacob was the founder of a whole new nation thanks to the number of

Bible began, Jacob lived in the land of Canaan, a
children he'd had. He was also known as Israel but most of the time his

Ze - bu - lun and Gad took the to - tal to nine.___ Ja - cob, Ja - cob and Sons,___

Ben - ja - min and Ju - dah, which leaves on - ly one,___ Ja - cob, Ja - cob and Sons,___

Jo - seph, Ja - cob's fa - vour - ite son.___ Ja - cob, Ja - cob and Sons,___

Ja - cob, Ja - cob and Sons,___ Ja - cob, Ja - cob and Sons,___

Joseph's Dreams

Music by ANDREW LLOYD WEBBER

Lyrics by TIM RICE

seems to us that Jo - seph and his dreams should dis - ap - pear. I
dreamed I saw e - le - ven stars, the sun and moon and sky,
bow - ing down be - fore my star, it made me won - der why.
Could it be that I was born for high - er things than you? A
post in some - one's go - vern - ment, a mi - ni - stry or two? The

JOSEPH

BROTHERS

Poor, Poor Joseph

Music by ANDREW LLOYD WEBBER

Lyrics by TIM RICE

One More Angel In Heaven

Music by ANDREW LLOYD WEBBER

Lyrics by TIM RICE

Potiphar

Music by ANDREW LLOYD WEBBER

Lyrics by TIM RICE

Jo - seph was ta - ken to E - gypt in chains and sold,

poco a poco accel.

Joseph was an un-im-por-tant slave who found he liked his mas-ter,
Joseph's looks and hand-some fi-gure had at-tract-ed her at-ten-tion,

v.2 MRS POTIPHAR

con-se-quent-ly worked much hard-er, ev-en with de-vo-tin.
ev-'ry morn-ing she would beck-on Come and lie with me, love.

v.2 NARRATOR

Pot-i-phar could see that Jo-seph, was a cut a-bove the av-'rage, made him lea-der
Joseph want-ed to re-sist her, till one day she proved too ea-ger. Jo-seph cried in

1. Tempo 1   2. Tempo 1

v.2 JOSEPH

of his house-hold, max-i-mum pro-mo-tion.
vain Please stop! I don't be-lieve in free love.

3
(Cow-bell)

3
(Cow-bell)

sim.

3

poco a poco accel.

NARRATOR + CHOIR

Pot - i - phar was count - ing shek - els in his den be - low the bed - room

when he heard a might - y rum - pus clat - ter - ing a - bove him.

CLOSE EVERY DOOR

Music by ANDREW LLOYD WEBBER

Lyrics by TIM RICE

Go, Go, Go Joseph

Music by ANDREW LLOYD WEBBER

Lyrics by TIM RICE

Tempo I

72 G   C⁷   G   D⁷   Gm   Gm⁷

I tried to in - ter - pret but I had to give up._____
Give me the mes - sage__ but keep it con - cise.

76 Gm   F   E♭   D⁷   Gm
mp JOSEPH

Sad to say your dream is not the kind of dream I'd like to get.

80   F   E♭   D⁷   Gm

Phar - aoh has it in for you, your ex - e - cu - tion date is set.

84 B♭   F   C   G

Don't re - ly on all I said__ I saw,_____ it's

Tempo di Go-go

88 B♭   F   C   F   D   Cadd9
NARRATOR
f + CHORUS MEN *ad lib.*

just that I have not been wrong__ be - fore.   Go, go, go

56

ACT TWO

ENTR'ACTE

Music by ANDREW LLOYD WEBBER
Lyrics by TIM RICE

Pharaoh Story

Music by ANDREW LLOYD WEBBER

Lyrics by TIM RICE

Strange as it seems, there's been a run of cra-zy dreams,_ and a man who can in-ter-pret could go far, could be-come a star.___ Could be fa-mous, could be a big suc-cess, could be fa-mous, could be a big suc-cess.

POOR, POOR PHARAOH/SONG OF THE KING

Music by ANDREW LLOYD WEBBER

Lyrics by TIM RICE

Pharaoh's Dreams Explained

Music by ANDREW LLOYD WEBBER

Lyrics by TIM RICE

STONE THE CROWS

Music by ANDREW LLOYD WEBBER

Lyrics by TIM RICE

Pharaoh said, Well stone the crows, this Joseph is a clever kid. Who'd have thought that fourteen cows could mean the things he said they did. Joseph, you must help me further, I have found a job for you. You shall lead us through this crisis. You shall be my number two. Pharaoh told his guards to fetch a chisel from the local store, whereupon he ordered them to cut the chains that Joseph wore. Joseph got a royal pardon

King Of My Heart

Music by ANDREW LLOYD WEBBER

Lyrics by TIM RICE

STONE THE CROWS
(PART TWO)

Music by ANDREW LLOYD WEBBER

Lyrics by TIM RICE

This could be a hap-py end-ing, per-fect place to stop the show, Jo-seph af-ter all has got a-

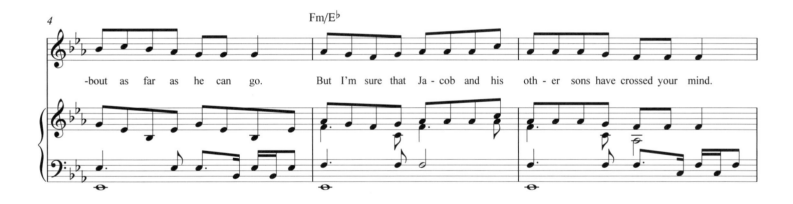

-bout as far as he can go. But I'm sure that Ja-cob and his oth-er sons have crossed your mind.

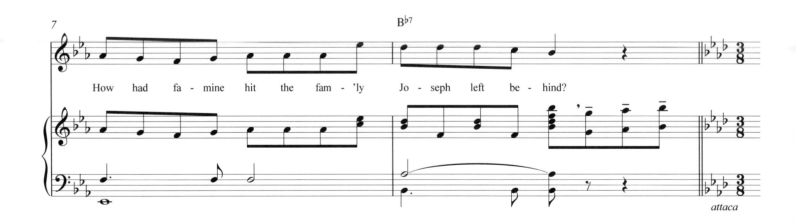

How had fa-mine hit the fam-'ly Jo-seph left be-hind?

attaca

THOSE CANAAN DAYS

Music by ANDREW LLOYD WEBBER

Lyrics by TIM RICE

THE BROTHERS COME TO EGYPT/GROVEL, GROVEL

Music by ANDREW LLOYD WEBBER

Lyrics by TIM RICE

Who's The Thief?

Music by ANDREW LLOYD WEBBER

Lyrics by TIM RICE

Benjamin Calypso

Music by ANDREW LLOYD WEBBER

Lyrics by TIM RICE

JOSEPH ALL THE TIME

Music by ANDREW LLOYD WEBBER
Lyrics by TIM RICE

JACOB IN EGYPT

Music by ANDREW LLOYD WEBBER

Lyrics by TIM RICE

ANY DREAM WILL DO

Music by ANDREW LLOYD WEBBER
Lyrics by TIM RICE

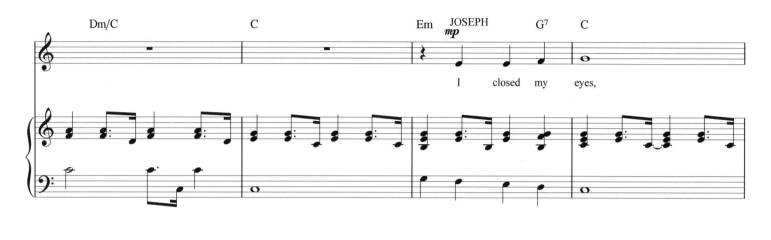

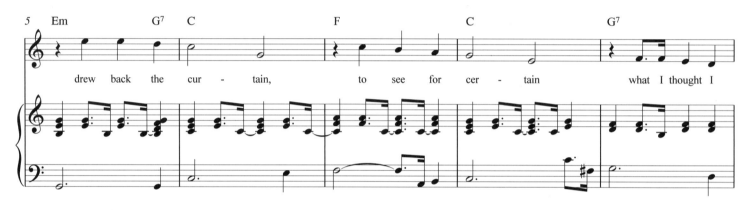

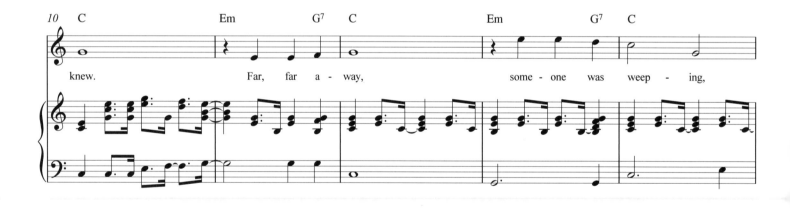

Printed in the EU - 4 5 6 7 8 9